Arranged for *all* electronic keyboards *by Kenneth Baker.*

# THE COMPLETE KEYBOARD PLAYER

# BEST SONGS FROM THE SHOWS

**Wise Publications**
**London/New York/Paris/Sydney/Copenhagen/Madrid/Tokyo**

Exclusive Distributors:
**Music Sales Limited**
14-15 Berners Street, London W1T 3LJ, UK.
**Music Sales Pty Limited**
20 Resolution Drive, Caringbah, NSW 2229, Australia.

This book © Copyright 2000 by
Wise Publications.
Order No. AM963920
ISBN 0-7119-8157-4

Compiled by Nick Crispin.
Music arranged by Kenneth Baker.
Music processed by Dakota Music Service.

Cover design by Michael Bell Design.
Photographs courtesy of Rex Features.

**Your Guarantee of Quality**
As publishers, we strive to produce every book
to the highest commercial standards.
The music has been freshly engraved and the book has been
carefully designed to minimise awkward page turns and to make
playing from it a real pleasure.
Particular care has been given to specifying acid-free, neutral-sized paper
made from pulps which have not been elemental chlorine bleached.
This pulp is from farmed sustainable forests and was produced with special
regard for the environment. Throughout, the printing and binding have been
planned to ensure a sturdy, attractive publication which should give years of enjoyment.
If your copy fails to meet our high standards, please inform us and
we will gladly replace it.

www.musicsales.com

Printed in the United Kingdom by
Printwise (Haverhill) Limited, Suffolk.

# GETTING TO KNOW YOU

## Lyrics by Oscar Hammerstein II. Music by Richard Rodgers

**Voice:** pan flute
**Rhythm:** swing
**Tempo:** medium (♩=120)

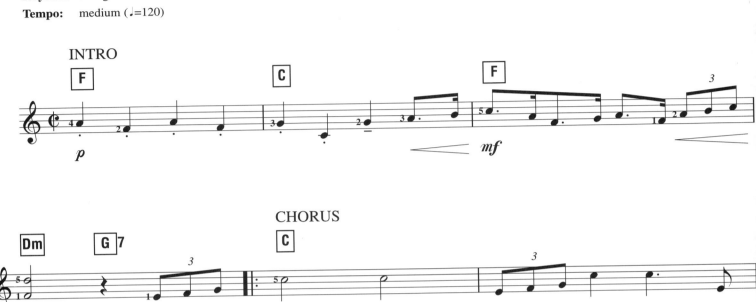

Get-ting to know you, get-ting to know all a-
know you, get-ting to feel free and

bout you.
ea - sy.

Get - ting to like you,
When I am like with you,

get-ting to hope you like me.
get-ting to know what to say.

Get-ting to
Have-n't you

know you, put-ting it my way, but nice - ly.

# DON'T CRY FOR ME ARGENTINA

Music by Andrew Lloyd Webber. Lyrics by Tim Rice

**Voice:** string ensemble
**Rhythm:** tango
**Tempo:** medium (♩=88)

VERSE

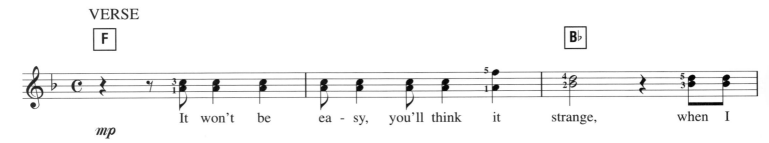

It won't be ea - sy, you'll think it strange, when I

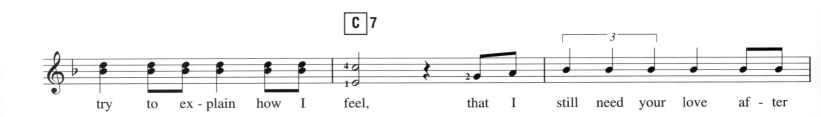

try to ex - plain how I feel, that I still need your love af - ter

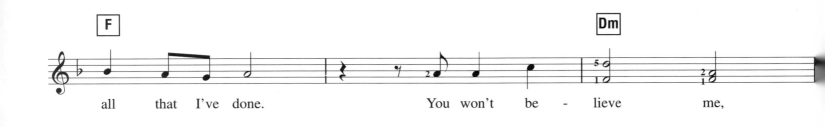

all that I've done. You won't be - lieve me,

all you will see is a girl you once knew, al - though she's dressed up to the

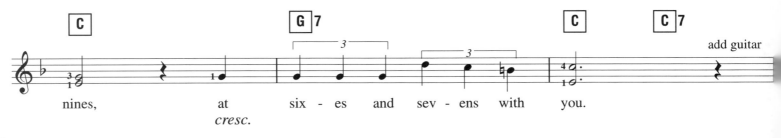

nines, at six - es and sev - ens with you.
*cresc.*

**CHORUS**

Don't cry for me, Ar - gen - ti - na, the truth is I nev - er

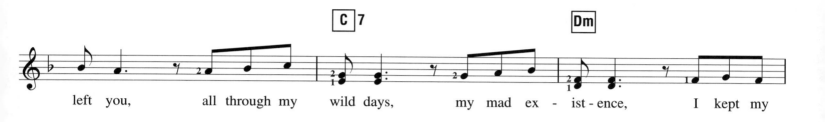

left you, all through my wild days, my mad ex - ist - ence, I kept my

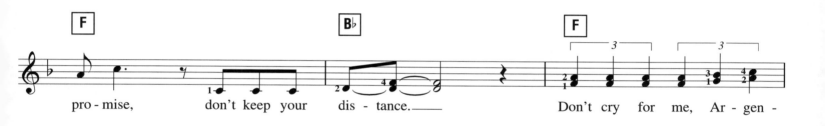

pro - mise, don't keep your dis - tance.___ Don't cry for me, Ar - gen -

ti - na, the truth is I nev - er left you, all through my

wild days, my mad ex - ist - ence, I kept my pro - mise, don't keep your

dis - tance.___

# PEOPLE WILL SAY WE'RE IN LOVE

Lyrics by Oscar Hammerstein II. Music by Richard Rodgers

**Voice:** flute

**Rhythm:** swing

**Tempo:** medium (♩=126)

say we're in love!

Don't start
*mp*

lect - ing things. Give me my

rose and my glove. *cresc.*

Sweet - heart, they're sus - pect - ing things,
*mf*

peo - ple will say we're in love.
*f*

stop rhythm

9

# NO MATTER WHAT

## Music by Andrew Lloyd Webber. Lyrics by Jim Steinman

**Voice:** string ensemble
**Rhythm:** 8 beat
**Tempo:** medium (♩=100)

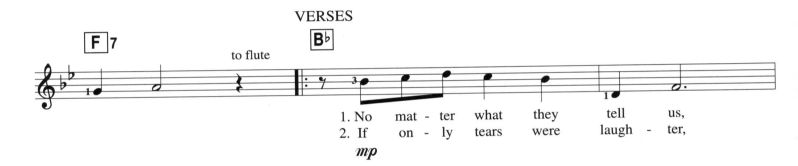

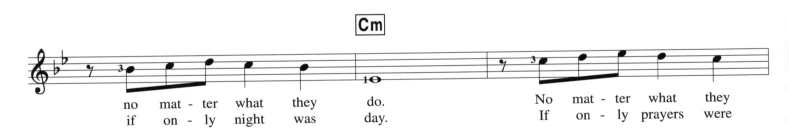

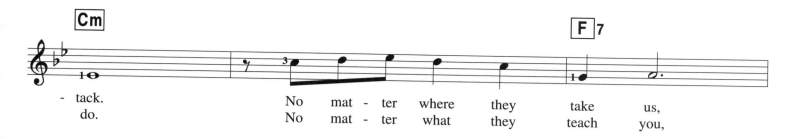

- tack.
do.

No mat - ter where they take us,
No mat - ter what they teach you,

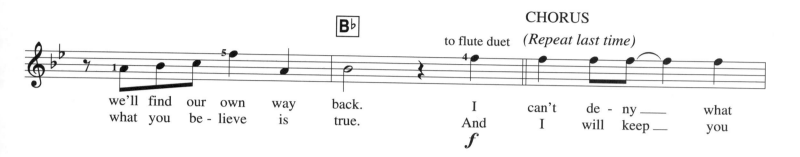

**CHORUS**

to flute duet  *(Repeat last time)*

we'll find our own way back.
what you be - lieve is true.

I can't de - ny ____ what
And I will keep ____ you

*f*

I be - lieve, ____
safe and strong, ____

I can't be ____ what I'm not. ____
and shel - tered ____ from the storm. ____

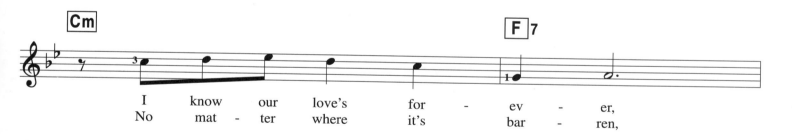

I know our love's for - ev - er,
No mat - ter where it's bar - ren,

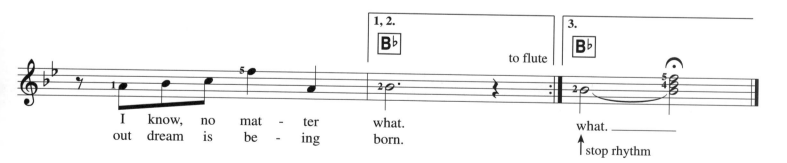

**1, 2.**

**3.**

to flute

I know, no mat - ter what.
out dream is be - ing born.

what. ____

↑ stop rhythm

3.
(INSTRUMENTAL 8 bars)
No matter who they follow,
No matter where they lead;
No matter how they judge us,
I'll be ev'ryone you need.

CHORUS
No matter if the sun don't shine,
Or if the skies are blue;
No matter what the ending,
My life began with you.
I can't deny what I believe,
I can't be what I'm not,
I know this love's forever,
I know, no matter what.

# SUNRISE, SUNSET

Lyrics by Sheldon Harnick. Music by Jerry Bock

**Voice:**    accordion
**Rhythm:**  waltz
**Tempo:**   fairly fast (♩=144)

Is this the lit-tle girl I car -
When did she get to be a beau -

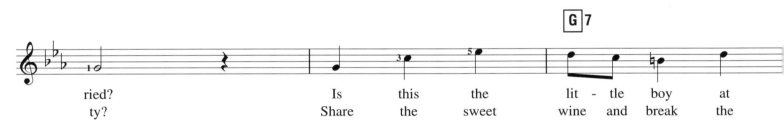

ried?          Is this the lit-tle boy at
ty?         Share the sweet wine and break the

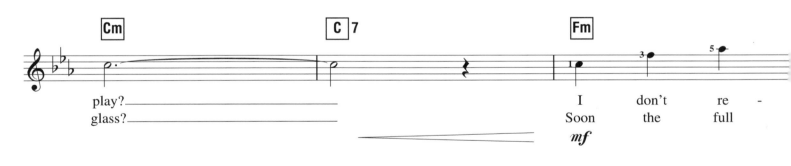

play?                 I don't re -
glass?               Soon the full

mem - ber grow - ing old - er,
cir - cle will have come

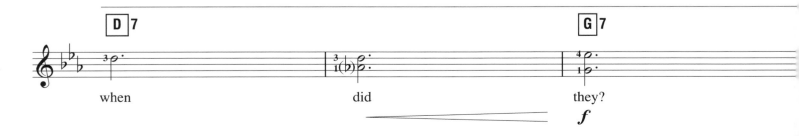

when did they?

# THE MUSIC OF THE NIGHT

Music by Andrew Lloyd Webber. Lyrics by Charles Hart
Additional Lyrics by Richard Stilgoe

**Voice:** clarinet
**Rhythm:** rhumba
**Tempo:** quite slow (♩=84)

Night - time shar - pens, height - ens each sen - sa - tion. Dark - ness stirs, and

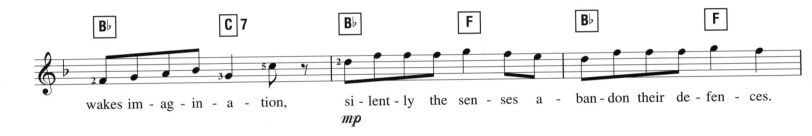

wakes im - ag - in - a - tion, si - lent - ly the sen - ses a - ban - don their de - fen - ces.

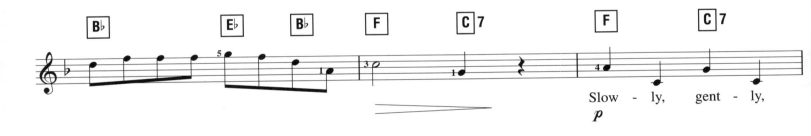

Slow - ly, gent - ly,

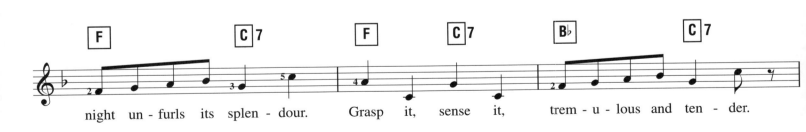

night un - furls its splen - dour. Grasp it, sense it, trem - u - lous and ten - der.

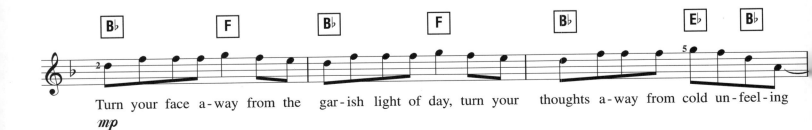

Turn your face a - way from the gar - ish light of day, turn your thoughts a - way from cold un - feel - ing

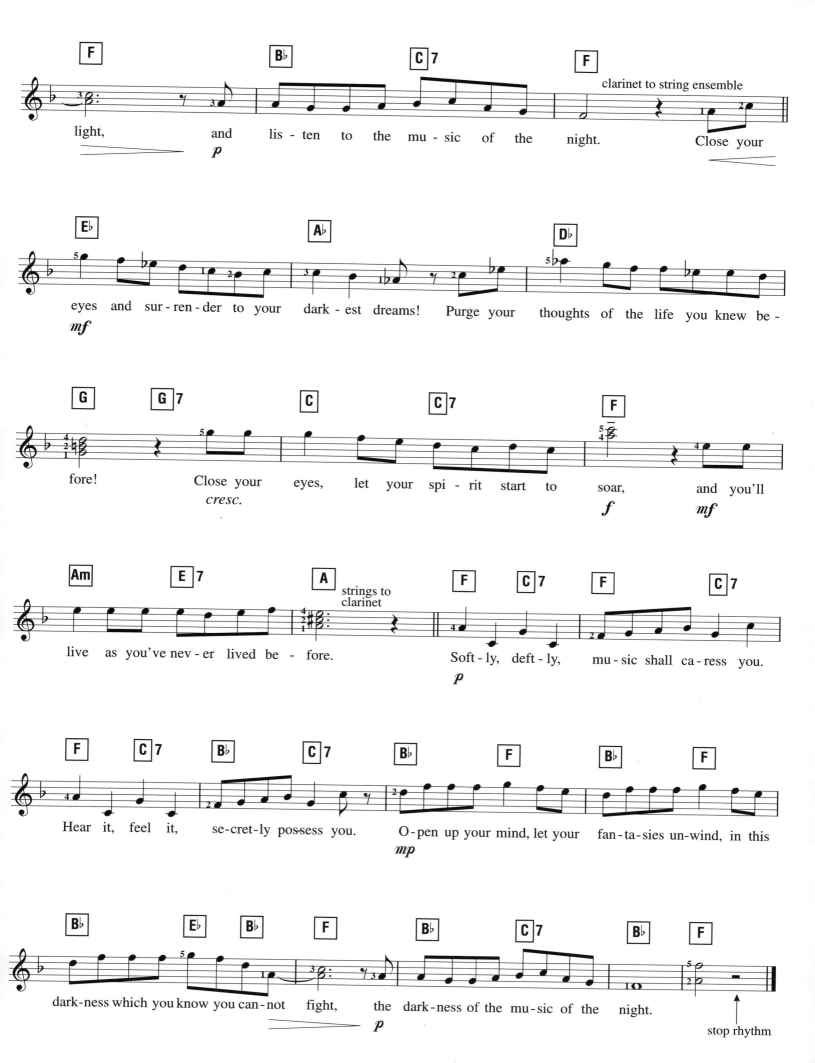

# CABARET

**Lyrics by Fred Ebb. Music by John Kander**

**Voice:** horn
**Rhythm:** swing
**Tempo:** fast (♩=160)

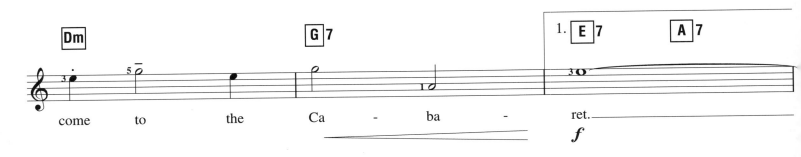

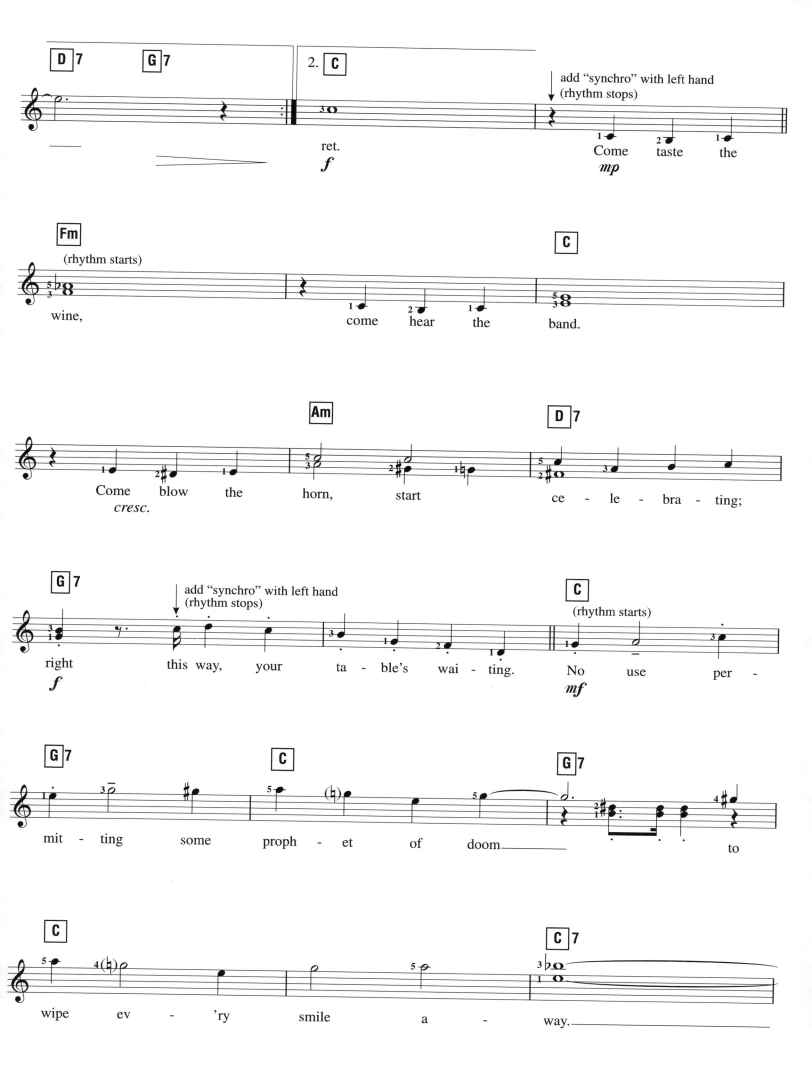

# SUN AND MOON

Music by Claude-Michel Schönberg. Lyrics by Richard Maltby Jr. & Alain Boublil
Adapted from the original French Lyrics by Alain Boublil

**Voice:**   human voice
**Rhythm:**  8 beat light
**Tempo:**   quite slow (♩=88)

(Kim) You are _____ sun - light _____ and I moon, _____

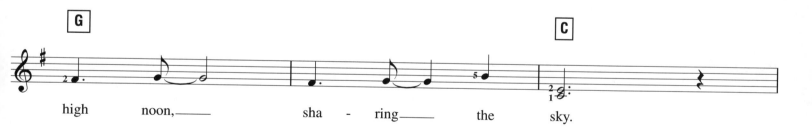

joined by _____ the gods of for - tune, _____ mid - night, _____ and

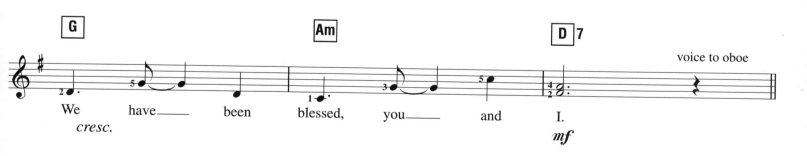

high noon, _____ sha - ring _____ the sky.

voice to oboe

We have _____ been blessed, you _____ and I.
cresc.                                     mf

(Chris) You came _____ here like _____ a my - s'try, _____
p

I'm from___ a world that's___ so diff - 'rent___ from
all that___ you are. How in___ the
light of___ one night did___ we come so
far? (Kim) Out - side___ day starts___ to
dawn. (Chris) Your moon___ still floats___ on
high. (Kim) The birds a - wake, (Chris) the stars shine too, (Kim) my

20

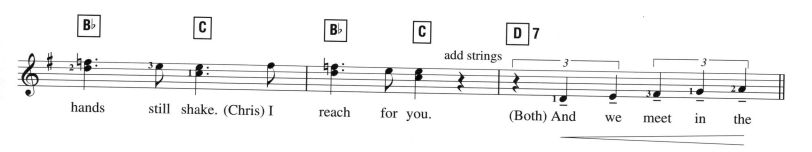

hands still shake. (Chris) I reach for you. (Both) And we meet in the

(Kim) You are____ sun - light,____ and I moon,____
sky.
*ff*

joined here,____ bright - 'ning____ the sky with____ the

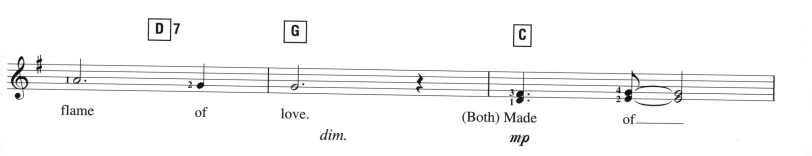

flame of love. (Both) Made of____
*dim.* *mp*

*Slower*

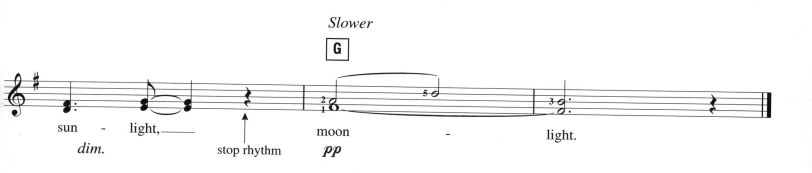

sun - light,____ moon - light.
*dim.* stop rhythm *pp*

21

# TELL ME IT'S NOT TRUE

Lyrics & Music by Willy Russell

**Voice:** flute
**Rhythm:** 8 beat
**Tempo:** fairly slow (♩=76)

VERSES

1. Tell me it's not true. Say it's just a
3. Tell me it's not true. Say I on - ly

sto - ry. Some-thing in the news. though it's here be -
dreamed it. Mor - ning will come soon.

Tell me it's not true, though it's here be -
Tell me it's not true, say you did - n't

fore me. Say it's just a dream, say it's just a scene
mean it. Say it's just pre - tend, say it's just the end

from an old mo - vie of years a - go; from an old mo - vie of
of an old mo - vie of years a - go; from an old mo - vie with

22

*to CODA* ⊕

Gm     C7     B♭     C7     F     Am

flute to piano

Ma - ri - lyn____ Mon - roe.____
Ma - ri - lyn____ Mon - roe.____ 2. Say it's just some
*mp*

B♭     C7     F     Am     B♭     C7

clowns, two play - ers in the lime - light. And

Am     B♭     C7     F     Am     B♭     C7

bring the cur - tain down.____ Say it's just two clowns who

F     Am     B♭     C7     Am     Dm

could - n't get their lives____ right. Say it's just a show
*mf*

C     F     B♭     Gm     C7

on the ra - di - o,____ that we can turn o - ver, and start____ a - gain; that

*D.C. al CODA* ⊕ CODA *D.C. and fade ad lib.*

Dm     B♭     Gm     C7     B♭     C7     B♭     C7

piano to flute

we can turn o - ver, it's on - ly a game.____

# CLIMB EV'RY MOUNTAIN

## Lyrics by Oscar Hammerstein II. Music by Richard Rodgers

**Voice:** violin solo
**Rhythm:** 8 beat light
**Tempo:** medium (♩=88)

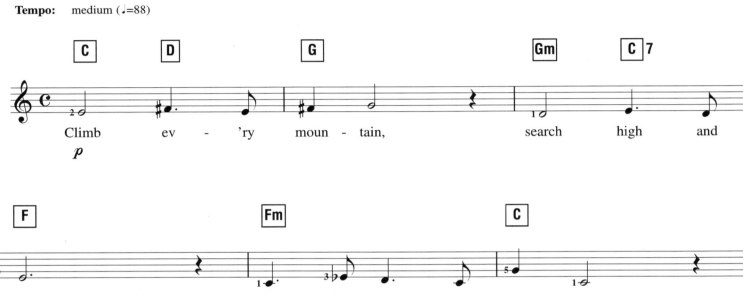

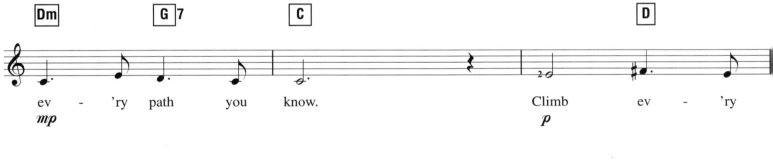

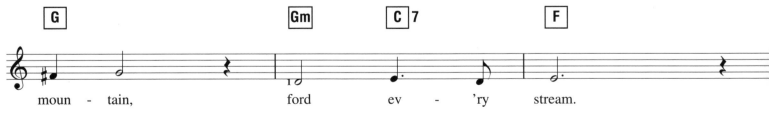

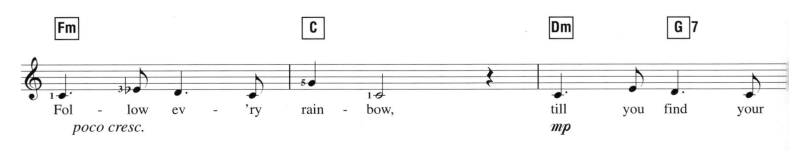

# PICK A POCKET OR TWO

Lyrics and Music by Lionel Bart

**Voice:**   brass ensemble
**Rhythm:**   quickstep
**Tempo:**   fast (♩=175)

INTRO

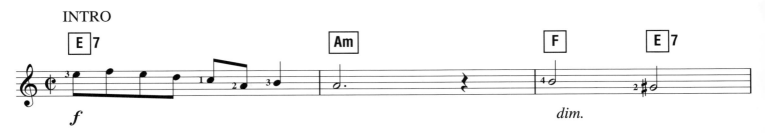

VERSES

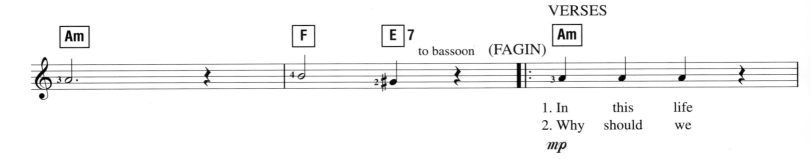

1. In this life
2. Why should we

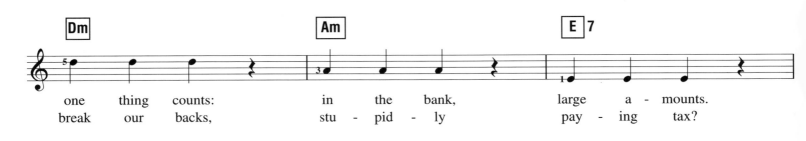

one thing counts:  in the bank,  large a - mounts.
break our backs,  stu - pid - ly  pay - ing tax?

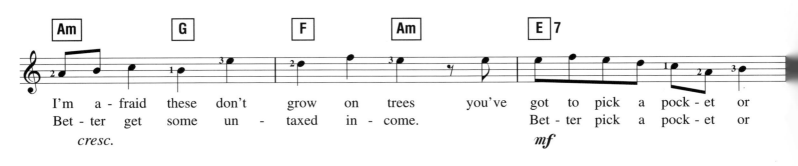

I'm a - fraid these don't grow on trees  you've got to pick a pock - et or
Bet - ter get some un - taxed in - come.  Bet - ter pick a pock - et or

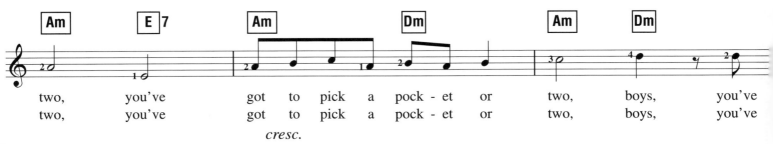

two,  you've  got to pick a pock - et or  two,  boys,  you've
two,  you've  got to pick a pock - et or  two,  boys,  you've

3. (Fagin) Robin Hood, what a crook!
   Gave away what he took.
   Charity's fine, subscribe to mine,
   Get out and pick a pocket or two.
   You've got to pick a pocket or two, boys,
   You've got to pick a pocket or two.
   (Boys) Robin Hood was far too good,
   Get out and pick a pocket or two.

4. (Fagin) Take a tip from Bill Sykes,
   He can whip what he likes.
   I recall he started small,
   He had to pick a pocket or two!
   You've got to pick a pocket or two, boys,
   You've got to pick a pocket or two.
   (Boys) We can be like old Bill Sykes,
   If we pick a pocket or two.

5. (Fagin) Dear old gent, passing by,
   Something nice takes his eye.
   Ev'rything's clear! Attack the rear!
   Advance and pick a pocket or two.
   You've got to pick a pocket or two, boys,
   You've got to pick a pocket or two.
   (Boys) Have no fear, attack the rear,
   Get in and pick a pocket or two.

6. (Fagin) When I see someone rich
   Both my thumbs start to itch.
   Only to find some peace of mind,
   I have to pick a pocket or two.
   You've got to pick a pocket or two, boys,
   You've got to pick a pocket or two.
   (Boys) Just to find some peace of mind,
   We have to pick a pocket or two!

27

# LOVE CHANGES EVERYTHING

Music by Andrew Lloyd Webber. Lyrics by Don Black & Charles Hart

**Voice:** pan flute
**Rhythm:** 8 beat
**Tempo:** medium (♩=92)

# I DREAMED A DREAM

Lyrics by Herbert Kretzmer. Music by Claude-Michel Schönberg
Original Text by Alain Boublil & Jean-Marc Natel

**Voice:**    string ensemble
**Rhythm:**    rock
**Tempo:**    fairly slow (♩=80)

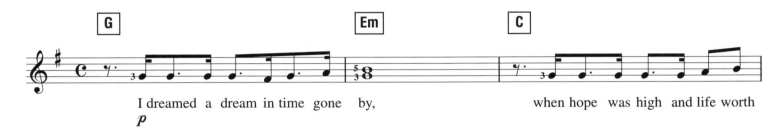

I dreamed a dream in time gone by, when hope was high and life worth

li - ving. I dreamed that love would ne - ver die,

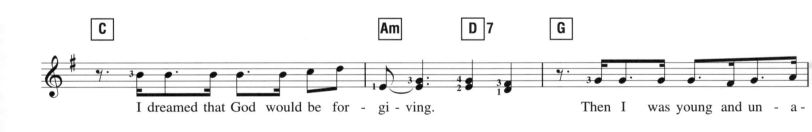

I dreamed that God would be for - gi - ving. Then I was young and un - a-

fraid, when dreams were made and used and was - ted.

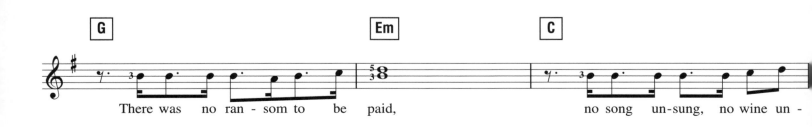

There was no ran - som to be paid, no song un - sung, no wine un-

tas - ted._____ But the ti - gers come at night, with their voi - ces soft as thun - der._____ As they tear your hope a - part, as they turn your dream to shame. He slept a sum - mer by my side, he filled my days with end - less won - der. He took my child - hood in his stride, but he was gone when Au - tumn came.

add flute  
*mf*

*p  cresc.*

cut flute  
*f*  
*p*

*cresc.*  
*f*

stop rhythm

# OL' MAN RIVER

Lyrics by Oscar Hammerstein II. Music by Jerome Kern

**Voice:** clarinet
**Rhythm:** rhumba
**Tempo:** slow (♩=76)

# BIG SPENDER

### Lyrics by Dorothy Fields. Music by Cy Coleman

**Voice:** trumpet
**Rhythm:** swing
**Tempo:** medium (♩=108)
**Synchro:** on

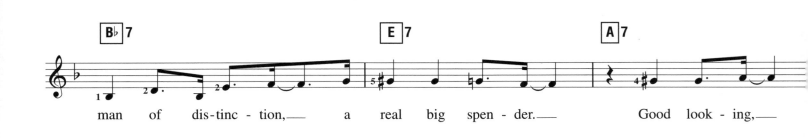

The min-ute you walked in the joint, I could see you were a man of dis-tinc-tion,— a real big spen-der.— Good look-ing,—

so re-fined,— say would-n't you like to know what's go-ing on in my mind? So let me get

right to the point. I don't pop my cork for ev-'ry guy I see.

# ANTHEM

### Lyrics & Music by Benny Andersson, Tim Rice & Björn Ulvaeus

**Voice:** oboe
**Rhythm:** 8 beat
**Tempo:** quite slow (♩=84)

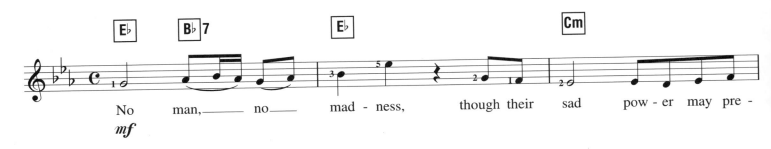

No man,⎯⎯ no⎯⎯ mad - ness, though their sad pow - er may pre -

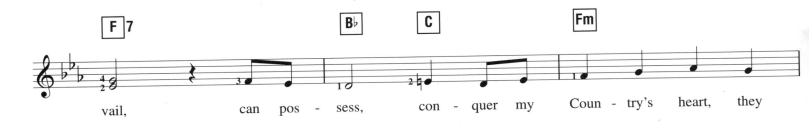

vail, can pos - sess, con - quer my Coun - try's heart, they

rise to fail. She is⎯⎯ e -

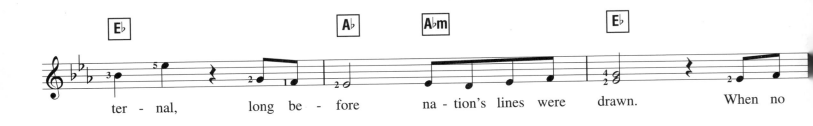

ter - nal, long be - fore na - tion's lines were drawn. When no

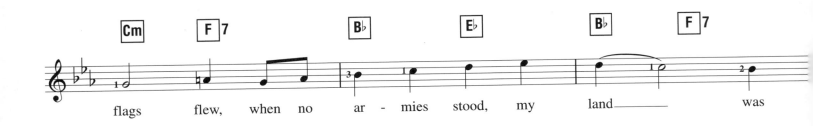

flags flew, when no ar - mies stood, my land⎯⎯ was

born.     And     you     ask     me     why     I     love     her     through

wars,     death     and     des - pair.     She     is     the

con - stant,     we     who     don't     care.     And

you     won - der,     will     I     leave     her,     but     how?

I     cross     o - ver     bor - ders,     but     I'm

INSTRUMENTAL

to brass ensemble

still     there     now.

37

VOCAL

to oboe

*mp*

How    can    I    leave    her?

Where    would    I    start?    Let    man's    pet - ty

na - tions tear them - selves____ a - part.    My    land's on - ly
*mf  cresc.*

bor - ders    lie    a - round____    my    heart.____
*f*

stop rhythm

# CHORD CHARTS (For Left Hand)

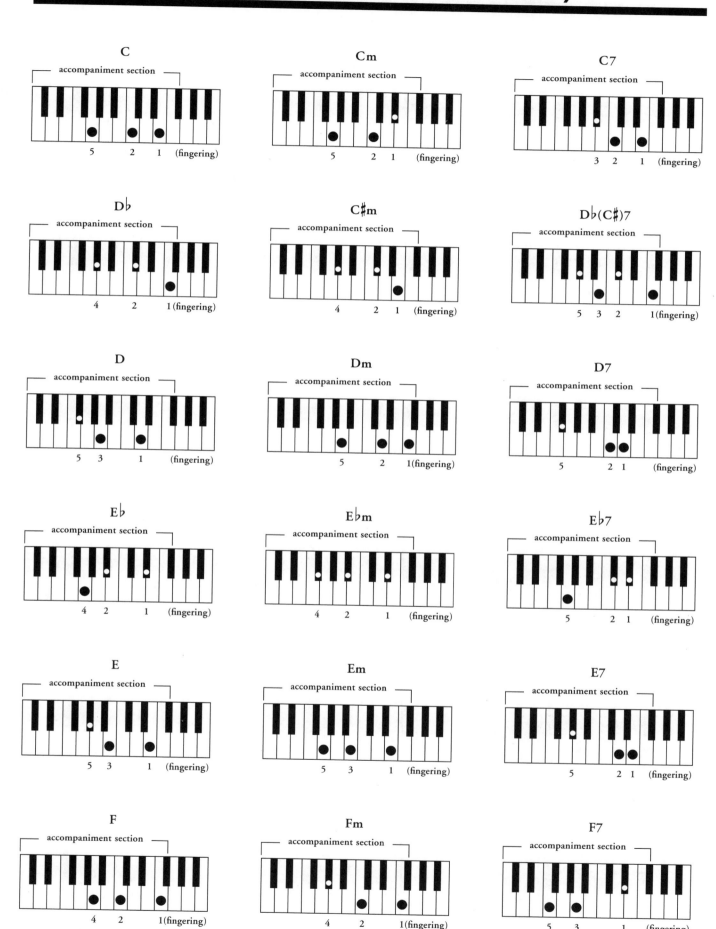

# CHORD CHARTS (For Left Hand)

### G♭(F♯)
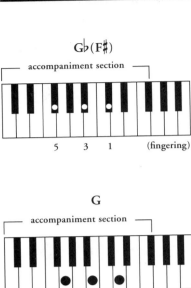
accompaniment section

5  3  1  (fingering)

### F♯m
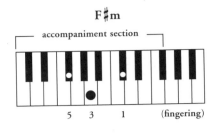
accompaniment section

5  3  1  (fingering)

### G♭(F♯)7
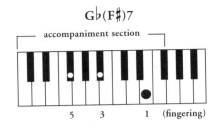
accompaniment section

5  3  1  (fingering)

### G
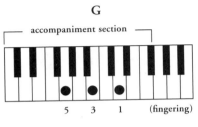
accompaniment section

5  3  1  (fingering)

### Gm
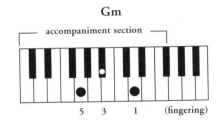
accompaniment section

5  3  1  (fingering)

### G7
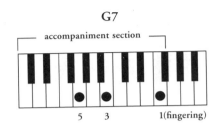
accompaniment section

5  3  1(fingering)

### A♭
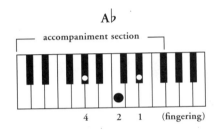
accompaniment section

4  2  1  (fingering)

### A♭m
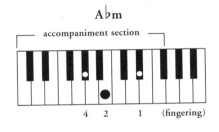
accompaniment section

4  2  1  (fingering)

### A♭7
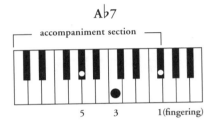
accompaniment section

5  3  1(fingering)

### A
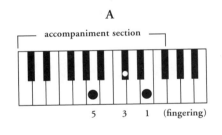
accompaniment section

5  3  1  (fingering)

### Am
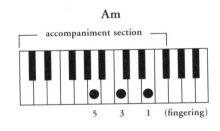
accompaniment section

5  3  1  (fingering)

### A7
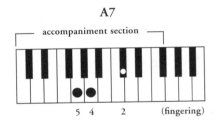
accompaniment section

5  4  2  (fingering)

### B♭
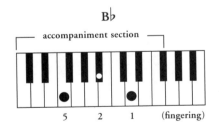
accompaniment section

5  2  1  (fingering)

### B♭m
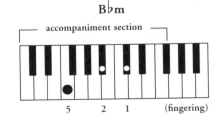
accompaniment section

5  2  1  (fingering)

### B♭7
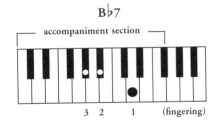
accompaniment section

3  2  1  (fingering)

### B
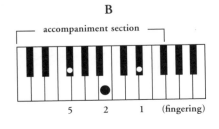
accompaniment section

5  2  1  (fingering)

### Bm
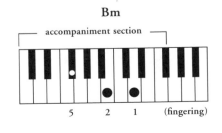
accompaniment section

5  2  1  (fingering)

### B7
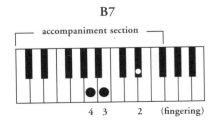
accompaniment section

4  3  2  (fingering)

3/08 (165307)